AN

ESSAY

ON THE

SHAKING PALSY

JAMES PARKINSON

London 1817

For those who search

for ways to make life

◆

better for people

◆

living with

◆

Parkinson's disease—

◆

A gift of appreciation

SINEMET® CR
(CARBIDOPA-LEVODOPA)
SUSTAINED-RELEASE

AN

ESSAY

ON THE

SHAKING PALSY.

———

BY

JAMES PARKINSON,
MEMBER OF THE ROYAL COLLEGE OF SURGEONS.

———

LONDON:
PRINTED BY WHITTINGHAM AND ROWLAND,
Goswell Street,

FOR SHERWOOD, NEELY, AND JONES,
PATERNOSTER ROW.
1817.

PREFACE.

THE advantages which have been derived from the caution with which hypothetical statements are admitted, are in no instance more obvious than in those sciences which more particularly belong to the healing art. It therefore is necessary, that some conciliatory explanation should be offered for the present publication: in which, it is acknowledged, that mere conjecture takes the place of experiment; and, that analogy is the substitute for anatomical examination, the only sure foundation for pathological knowledge.

When, however, the nature of the subject and the circumstances under which it has been here taken up, are considered, it is

hoped that the offering of the following pages
to the attention of the medical public, will
not be severely censured. The disease, respecting which the present inquiry is made,
is of a nature highly afflictive. Notwithstanding which, it has not yet obtained a
place in the classification of nosologists;
some have regarded its characteristic symptoms as distinct and different diseases, and
others have given its name to diseases differing essentially from it; whilst the unhappy
sufferer has considered it as an evil, from the
domination of which he had no prospect of
escape.

The disease is of long duration : to con-
nect, therefore, the symptoms which occur
in its later stages with those which mark its
commencement, requires a continuance of
observation of the same case, or at least a
correct history of its symptoms, even for
several years. Of both these advantages
the writer has had the opportunities of avail-

ing himself; and has hence been led particularly to observe several other cases in
which the disease existed in different stages
of its progress. By these repeated observations, he hoped that he had been led to a
probable conjecture as to the nature of the
malady, and that analogy had suggested such
means as might be productive of relief, and
perhaps even of cure, if employed before
the disease had been too long established.
He therefore considered it to be a duty to
submit his opinions to the examination of
others, even in their present state of imma-
turity and imperfection.

To delay their publication did not, indeed,
appear to be warrantable. The disease had
escaped particular notice; and the task of
ascertaining its nature and cause by anatomical investigation, did not seem likely to be
taken up by those who, from their abilities
and opportunities, were most likely to ac-
complish it. That these friends to huma-

nity and medical science, who have already
unveiled to us many of the morbid processes
by which health and life is abridged, might
be excited to extend their researches to this
malady, was much desired; and it was hoped,
that this might be procured by the publication of these remarks.

Should the necessary information be thus
obtained, the writer will repine at no cen-
sure which the precipitate publication of
mere conjectural suggestions may incur;
but shall think himself fully rewarded by
having excited the attention of those, who
may point out the most appropriate means
of relieving a tedious and most distressing
malady.

CONTENTS.

AN

ESSAY

ON THE

SHAKING PALSY.

═══════

CHAPTER I.

DEFINITION—HISTORY—ILLUSTRATIVE CASES.

═══════

SHAKING PALSY. *(Paralysis Agitans.)*

Involuntary tremulous motion, with lessened muscular power, in parts not in action and even when supported ; with a propensity to bend the trunk forward, and to pass from a walking to a running pace : the senses and intellects being uninjured.

THE term Shaking Palsy has been vaguely employed by medical writers in general. By some it has been used to designate or-

B

dinary cases of Palsy, in which some slight
tremblings have occurred; whilst by others
it has been applied to certain anomalous affections, not belonging to Palsy.

The shaking of the limbs belonging to this
disease was particularly noticed, as will be
seen when treating of the symptoms, by
Galen, who marked its peculiar character
by an appropriate term. The same symptom, it will also be seen, was accurately
treated of by Sylvius de la Boe. Juncker
also seems to have referred to this symptom : having divided tremor into active and
passive, he says of the latter, " ad affectus
semiparalyticos pertinent; de qualibus hic
agimus, quique *tremores paralytoidei* vocan-
tur." Tremor has been adopted, as a genus,
by almost every nosologist; but always un-
marked, in their several definitions, by such
characters as would embrace this disease.
The celebrated Cullen, with his accustomed
accuracy observes, " Tremorem, utpote sem-
per symptomaticum, in numerum generum
recipere nollem; species autem a Sauvagesio
recensitas, prout mihi vel astheniæ vel paraly-
sios, vel convulsionis symptomata esse viden-

tur, his subjungam*. Tremor can indeed only
be considered as a symptom, although several species of it must be admitted. In the
present instance, the agitation produced by
the peculiar species of tremor, which here
occurs, is chosen to furnish the epithet by
which this species of Palsy, may be distinguished.

HISTORY.

So slight and nearly imperceptible are
the first inroads of this malady, and so extremely slow is its progress, that it rarely
happens, that the patient can form any re-
collection of the precise period of its commencement. The first symptoms perceived
are, a slight sense of weakness, with a prone-
ness to trembling in some particular part;
sometimes in the head, but most commonly
in one of the hands and arms. These
symptoms gradually increase in the part
first affected; and at an uncertain period,
but seldom in less than twelvemonths or
more, the morbid influence is felt in some
other part. Thus assuming one of the

---

* Synopsis Nosologiæ Methodicæ.—Tom. ii. p. 195.

hands and arms to be first attacked, the other, at this period becomes similarly affected. After a few more months the patient is found to be less strict than usual in preserving an upright posture : this being most observable whilst walking, but sometimes whilst sitting or standing. Sometime after the appearance of this symptom, and during its slow increase, one of the legs is discovered slightly to tremble, and is also found to suffer fatigue sooner than the leg of the other side : and in a few months this limb becomes agitated by similar tremblings, and suffers a similar loss of power.

Hitherto the patient will have experienced but little inconvenience; and befriended by the strong influence of habitual endurance, would perhaps seldom think of his being the subject of disease, except when reminded of it by the unsteadiness of his hand, whilst writing or employing himself in any nicer kind of manipulation. But as the disease proceeds, similar employments are accomplished with considerable difficulty, the hand failing to answer with exactness to the dictates of the will. Walking becomes a task which cannot be performed without considerable attention. The legs are not raised to that height, or with that promptitude which the will directs, so that the utmost care is necessary to prevent frequent falls.

At this period the patient experiences much inconvenience, which unhappily is found daily to increase. The submission of the limbs to the directions of the will can hardly ever be obtained in the performance of the most ordinary offices of life. The fingers cannot be disposed of in the proposed directions, and applied with certainty to any proposed point. As time and the disease proceed, difficulties increase: writing can now be hardly at all accomplished; and reading, from the tremulous motion, is accomplished with some difficulty. Whilst at meals the fork not being duly directed frequently fails to raise the morsel from the plate : which, when seized, is with much difficulty conveyed to the mouth. At this period the patient seldom experiences a suspension of the agitation of his limbs. Commencing, for instance in one arm, the wearisome agitation is borne until beyond sufferance, when by suddenly changing the posture it is for a time stopped in that limb, to commence, generally, in less than a minute in one of the legs, or in the arm of the other side. Harassed by this tormenting round, the patient has recourse to walking, a mode of exercise to which the sufferers from this malady are in general partial; owing to their attention being thereby somewhat diverted from their unpleasant feelings, by the care and exertion required to ensure its safe performance.

But as the malady proceeds, even this temporary mitigation of suffering from the agitation of the limbs is denied. The propensity to lean forward becomes invincible, and the patient is thereby forced to step on the toes and fore part of the feet, whilst the upper part of the body is thrown so far forward as to render it difficult to avoid falling on the face. In some cases, when this state of the malady is attained, the patient can no longer exercise himself by walking in his usual manner, but is thrown on the toes and forepart of the feet; being, at the same time, irresistibly impelled to take much quicker and shorter steps, and thereby to adopt unwillingly a running pace. In some cases it is found necessary entirely to substitute running for walking; since otherwise the patient, on proceeding only a very few paces, would inevitably fall.

In this stage, the sleep becomes much disturbed. The tremulous motion of the limbs occur during sleep, and augment until they awaken the patient, and frequently with much agitation and alarm. The power of conveying the food to the mouth is at length so much impeded that he is obliged to consent to be fed by others. The bowels, which had been all along torpid, now, in most cases, demand stimulating medicines of very considerable power: the expulsion of the fæces from the rectum sometimes requiring mechanical aid. As the disease proceeds towards its last stage, the trunk is almost permanently bowed, the muscular power is more decidedly diminished, and the tremulous agitation becomes violent. The patient walks now with great difficulty, and unable any longer to support himself with his stick, he dares not venture on this exercise, unless assisted by an attendant, who walking backwards before him, prevents his falling forwards, by the pressure of his hands against the fore part of his shoulders. His words are now scarcely intelligible; and he is not only no longer able to feed himself, but when the food is conveyed to the mouth, so much are the actions of the muscles of the tongue, pharynx, &c. impeded by impaired action and perpetual agitation, that the food is with difficulty retained in the mouth until masticated; and then as difficultly swallowed. Now also, from the same cause, another very unpleasant circumstance occurs: the saliva fails of being directed to the back part of the fauces, and hence is continually draining from the mouth, mixed with the particles of food, which he is no longer able to clear from the inside of the mouth.

As the debility increases and the influence of the will over the muscles fades away, the tremulous agitation becomes more vehement. It now seldom leaves him for a moment; but even when exhausted nature seizes a small portion of sleep, the motion becomes so violent as not only to shake the bed-hangings, but even the floor and sashes of the room. The chin is now almost immoveably bent down upon the sternum. The slops with which he is attempted to be fed, with the saliva, are continually trickling from the mouth. The power of articulation is lost. The urine and fæces are passed involuntarily; and at the last, constant sleepiness, with slight delirium, and other marks of extreme exhaustion, announce the wished-for release.

Case I.

Almost every circumstance noted in the preceding description, was observed in a case which occurred several years back, and which, from the particular symptoms which manifested themselves in its progress; from the little knowledge of its nature, acknowledged to be possessed by the physician who attended; and from the mode of its termination; excited an eager wish to acquire some further knowledge of its nature and cause.

c

The subject of this case was a man rather
more than fifty years of age, who had in-
dustriously followed the business of a gar-
dener, leading a life of remarkable temperance and sobriety. The commencement of
the malady was first manifested by a slight
trembling of the left hand and arm, a circumstance which he was disposed to attri-
bute to his having been engaged for several
days in a kind of employment requiring
considerable exertion of that limb. Although
repeatedly questioned, he could recollect no
other circumstance which he could consider
as having been likely to have occasioned his
malady. He had not suffered much from
Rheumatism, or been subject to pains of the
head, or had ever experienced any sudden
seizure which could be refered to apoplexy
or hemiplegia. In this case, every circumstance occurred which has been mentioned
in the preceding history.

Case II.

The subject of the case which was next
noticed was casually met with in the street.
It was a man sixty-two years of age; the

greater part of whose life had been spent as an attendant at a magistrate's office. He had suffered from the disease about eight or ten years. All the extremities were considerably agitated, the speech was very much interrupted, and the body much bowed and shaken. He walked almost entirely on the fore part of his feet, and would have fallen every step if he had not been supported by his stick. He described the disease as having come on very gradually, and as being, according to his full assurance, the consequence of considerable irregularities in his mode of living, and particularly of indulgence in spirituous liquors. He was the inmate of a poor-house of a distant parish, and being fully assured of the incurable nature of his complaint, declined making any attempts for relief.

Case III.

The next case was also noticed casually in the street. The subject of it was a man of about sixty-five years of age, of a remarkable athletic frame. The agitation of the limbs, and indeed of the head and of the whole body, was too vehement to allow it to be designated as trembling. He was entirely unable to walk; the body being so bowed, and the head thrown so forward, as to oblige him to go on a continued run, and to employ his stick every five or six steps to force him more into an upright posture, by projecting the point of it with great force against the pavement. He stated, that he had been a sailor, and attributed his complaints to having been for several months confined in a Spanish prison, where he had, during the whole period of his confinement, lain upon the bare damp earth. The disease had here continued so long, and made such a progress, as to afford little or no prospect of relief. He besides was a poor mendicant, requiring as well as the means of medical experiment, those collateral aids which he could only obtain in an hospital. He was therefore recommended to make trial if any relief could, in that mode, be yielded him. The poor man, however, appeared to be by no means disposed to make the experiment.

Case IV.

The next case which presented itself was that of a gentleman about fifty-five years, who had first experienced the trembling of the arms about five years before. His application was on account of a considerable degree of inflammation over the lower ribs on the left side, which terminated in the formation of matter beneath the fascia. About a pint was removed on making the necessary opening; and a considerable quantity discharged daily for two or three weeks. On his recovery from this, no change appeared to have taken place in his original complaint; and the opportunity of learning its future progress was lost by his removal to a distant part of the country.

Case V.

In another case, the particulars of which could not be obtained, and the gentleman, the lamented subject of which was only seen at a distance, one of the characteristic symptoms of this malady, the inability for motion, except in a running pace, appeared to exist in an extraordinary degree. It seemed to be necessary that the gentleman should be supported by his attendant, standing before him with a hand placed on each shoulder, until, by gently swaying backward and forward, he had placed himself in equipoise; when, giving the word, he would start in a running pace, the attendant sliding from before him and running forward, being ready to receive him and prevent his falling, after his having run about twenty paces.

Case VI.

In a case which presented itself to observation since those above-mentioned, every information as to the progress of the malady was very readily obtained. The gentleman who was the subject of it is seventy-two years of age. He has led a life of temperance, and has never been exposed to any particular situation or circumstance which he can conceive likely to have occasioned, or disposed to this complaint; which he rather seems to regard as incidental upon his advanced age, than as an object of medical attention. He however recollects, that about twenty years ago, he was troubled

with lumbago, which was severe and lasted
some time. About eleven or twelve, or
perhaps more, years ago, he first perceived
weakness in the left hand and arm, and
soon after found the trembling commence.
In about three years afterwards the right
arm became affected in a similar manner :
and soon afterwards the convulsive motions
affected the whole body, and began to in-
terrupt the speech. In about three years
from that time the legs became affected.
Of late years the action of the bowels
had been very much retarded; and at
two or three different periods had, with
great difficulty, been made to yield to the
action of very strong cathartics. But
within the last twelvemonths this difficulty
has not been so great; perhaps owing to
an increased secretion of mucus, which en-
velopes the passing fæces, and which pre-
cedes and follows their discharge in considerable quantity.

About a year since, on waking in the
night, he found that he had nearly lost the
use of the right side, and that the face was
much drawn to the left side. His medi-

cal attendant saw him the following day, when he found him languid, with a small and quick pulse, and without pain in the head or disposition to sleep. Nothing more therefore was done than to promote the action of the bowels, and apply a blister to the back of the neck, and in about a a fortnight the limbs had entirely recovered from their palsied state. During the time of their having remained in this state, neither the arm nor the leg of the paralytic side was in the least affected with the tremulous agitation; but as their paralysed state was removed, the shaking returned.

At present he is almost constantly troubled with the agitation, which he describes as generally commencing in a slight degree, and gradually increasing, until it arises to such a height as to shake the room; when, by a sudden and somewhat violent change of posture, he is almost always able to stop it. But very soon afterwards it will commence in some other limb, in a small degree, and gradually increase in violence; but he does not remember the thus checking of it, to have been followed by any injurious effect. When the agitation had not been thus interrupted, he stated, that it gradually extended through all the limbs, and at last affected the whole trunk. To illustrate his observation as to the power of suspending the motion by a sudden change of posture, he, being then just come in from a walk, with every limb shaking, threw himself rather violently into a chair, and said, " Now I am as well as ever I was in my life." The shaking completely stopped; but returned within two minutes' time.

He now possessed but little power in giving a required direction to the motions of any part. He was scarcely able to feed himself. He had written hardly intelligibly for the last three years; and at present could not write at all. His attendants observed, that of late the trembling would sometimes begin in his sleep, and increase until it awakened him : when he always was in a state of agitation and alarm.

On being asked if he walked under much apprehension of falling forwards? he said he suffered much from it; and replied in the

D

affirmative to the question, whether he experienced any difficulty in restraining himself from getting into a running pace ? It being asked, if whilst walking he felt much apprehension from the difficulty of raising his feet, if he saw a rising pebble in his path? he avowed, in a strong manner, his alarm on such occasions ; and it was observed by his wife, that she believed, that in walking across the room, he would consider as a difficulty the having to step over a pin.

The preceding cases appear to belong to the same species : differing from each other, perhaps, only in the length of time which the disease had existed, and the stage at which it had arrived.

CHAP. II.

IT has been seen in the preceding history of the disease, and in the accompanying cases, that certain affections, the tremulous agitations, and the almost invincible propensity to run, when wishing only to walk, each of which has been considered by nosologists as distinct diseases, appear to be pathognomonic symptoms of this malady. To determine in which of these points of view these affections ought to be regarded, an examination into their nature, and an inquiry into the opinions of preceding writers respecting them, seem necessary to be attempted.

———————

I. *Involuntary tremulous motion, with lessened voluntary muscular power, in parts, not in action, and even supported.*

IT is necessary that the peculiar nature of this tremulous motion should be ascertained, as well for the sake of giving to it its proper

JP—H

designation, as for assisting in forming probable conjectures, as to the nature of the
malady, which it helps to characterise.
Tremors were distinguished by Juncker into
Active, those proceeding from sudden affection of the minds, as terror, anger, &c. and
Passive, dependant on debilitating causes,
such as advanced age, palsy, &c*. But a
much more satisfactory and useful distinction is made by Sylvius de la Boë into those
tremors which are produced by attempts at
voluntary motion, and those which occur
whilst the body is at rest †. Sauvages distin-
guishes the latter of these species (*Tremor*

* Junckeri conspect. de tremore.

† Sect. v. Ubi autem solito pauciores deferunter ad
eadem organa spiritus animales, imperfectæ ac imbe-
cillæ observantur fieri eadem functiones, in motu tremulo et infirmo, nec diu durante, in visu debili, ac mox
defatigato, &c.

Sect. XIX. Inæqualiter, inordinatè, ac præter con-
traque voluntatem moventur spiritus animales per nervos ad partes mobiles, in motu convulsivo, ac tremore,
quassuve membrorum coacto.

Distinguendus namque his tremor quiescente licet ac
decumbente corpore molustus a motu tremulo, de quo
dictum. Sect. v. Quique quiescente corpore cessat,
eodemque iterum moto repetit.

Sect. XXV. Coactus tremor debetur animalibus spi-
ritibus inordinatè ac continuo, cum aliquo impetu ad

Coactus) by observing, that the tremulous
parts leap, and as it were vibrate, even when
supported : whilst every other tremor, he
observes, ceases, when the voluntary exertion for moving the limb stops, or the part is
supported, but returns when we will the limb
to move; whence, he says, tremor is distinguished from every other kind of spasm *.

A small degree of attention will be sufficient to perceive, that Sauvages, by this just
distinction, actually separates this kind of
tremulous motion, and which is the kind
peculiar to this disease, from the Genus Tremor. In doing this he is fully warranted
by the observations of Galen on the same
subject, as noticed by Van Swieten †.
" Binas has tremoris species‡ Galenus sub-

---

trementium membrorum musculos per nervos propulsis :
sive fuerit is universalis, sive particularis, sive corpus
fuerit ad huc robustum sive debile, Sylvii de la Boë.
Prax. lib. i. cap. xlii.

* Nosolog. Methodic. Auctore Fr. Boissier de Sauvages, Tomi. II. Partis ii. p. 54. 1763.

† Comment. in Herman. Boerhaav. Aphorismos.
Tom. ii. p. 181.

‡ De tremore. Cap. 3 and 4. Chart, Tom. vii. p.
200 201.

tiliter distinxit, atque etiam diversis nomini-
bus insignivit, tremor enim (τρόμ☾) facultatis
corpus moventis et vehentis infirmitate obo-
ritur. Quippe nemo, qui artus movere
non instituerit tremet. Palpitantes autem
partes, etiam in quiete fuerint, etiamsi nul-
lum illis motum induxeris palpitant. Ideo
primam (*posteriorem*) modo descriptam tremoris speciem, quando quiescenti homini
involuntariis illis et alternis motibus agitan-
tur membra, palpitationem (πάλμον) dixit,
posteriorem (*primam*) vero, quæ non fit
nisi homo conetur partes quasdam movere
tremorem vocavit."

Under this authority the term palpitation
may be employed to mark those morbid
motions which chiefly characterise this disease, notwithstanding that this term has
been anticipated by Sauvages, as characteristic of another species of tremor*. The

---

* Sect. xvi. *Tremor palpitans*, Preysinger classis
morborum. *Palmos* Galeni.

In tremoribus vulgaribus, æqualibus temporum inter-
vallis, non musculus, sed artus ipsemet alternatim at-
tollitur aut deprimitur, aut in oppositas partes it atque
redit per minima tamen spatiola; in palpitatione verè

separation of palpitation of the limbs (*Palmos* of Galen, *Tremor Coactus* of de la Boë) from tremor, is the more necessary to be insisted on, since the distinction may assist in leading to a knowledge of the seat of the disease. It is also necessary to bear in mind, that this affection is distinguishable from tremor, by the agitation, in the former, occurring whilst the affected part is supported and unemployed, and being even checked by the adoption of voluntary motion; whilst in the latter, the tremor is induced immediately on bringing the parts into action. Thus an artist, afflicted with the malady here treated of, whilst his hand and arm is palpitating strongly, will seize his pencil, and the motions will be suspended, allow-

sine ullo ordine musculi unius lacertus subito subsilit, nec regulariter continuoque movetur, sed nunc semel aut bis, nunc minimè intra idem tempus subsilit; an causa irritans in sensorio communi, an in musculo ipse palpitante Quærenda sit, ignoramus. *Nosologiæ Methodicæ*, Vol. I. p. 559. 1768.

But the adoption which Sauvages has made of this term, will not be regarded as an absolute prohibition from the employment of it here; since the *tremor palpitans* of Sauvages should be considered rather as a palpitation of the muscles, whilst the motion which is so prominent a symptom in this disease, may be considered as a palpitation of the limbs.

ing him to use it for a short period; but
in tremor, if the hand be quite free from
the affection, should the pen or pencil be
taken up, the trembling immediately com-
mences.

II. *A propensity to bend the trunk forwards, and to
pass from a walking to a running pace.*

THIS affection, which observation seems to
authorise the being considered as a symptom peculiar to this disease, has been mentioned by few nosologists: it appears to
have been first noticed by Gaubius, who
says, " Cases occur in which the muscles duly
excited into action by the impulse of the
will, do then, with an unbidden agility, and
with an impetus not to be repressed, acce-
lerate their motion, and run before the un-
willing mind. It is a frequent fault of the
muscles belonging to speech, nor yet of
these alone: I have seen one, who was able
to run, but not to walk * "

* Est et ubi musculi, recte quidem ad voluntatis
nutum in actum concitati, injussa dein agilitate atque
impetu non reprimendo motus suos accelerant, men-
temque invitam præcurrunt. Vitium loquelæ musculis

Sauvages, referring to this symptom, says, another disease which has been very rarely seen by authors, appears to be referable to the same genus (Scelotyrbe, of which he makes *Chorea sancti viti* the first species); which, he says, "I think cannot be more fitly named than hastening or hurrying Scelotyrbe (*Scelotyrbem festinantem, seu festiniam*)."

Scelotyrbe festinans, he says, is a peculiar species of scelotyrbe, in which the patients, whilst wishing to walk in the ordinary mode, are forced to run, which has been seen by Carguet and by the illustrious Gaubius; a similar affection of the speech, when the tongue thus outruns the mind, is termed volubility. Mons. de Sauvages attributes this complaint to a want of flexibility in the muscular fibres. Hence, he supposes, that the patients make shorter steps, and strive with a more than common exertion or impetus to overcome the resistance; walking with a quick and hastened step, as if hurried along against their will. *Chorea Viti,* he

frequens, nec his solis tamen proprium : vidi enim, qui currere, non gradi, poterat*.

* Institution. Patholog. Medicinal. Auctore. H. D. Gaubio. 751.

says, attacks the youth of both sexes, but
this disease only those advanced in years;
and adds, that it has hitherto happened to
him to have seen only two of these cases;
and that he has nothing to offer respecting
them, either in theory or practice*.

* Ad idem genus morbi altera species rarissima ab auc-
toribus prætervisa referenda videtur, quam non aptius
nominari posse putem quàm scelotyrbem festinantem,
seu festiniam.

SECT. II. *Scelotyrbe festinans;* est peculiaris scelo-
tyrbes species in qua ægri solito more dum gradi volunt
currere coguntur, quod videre est apud D. Carquet, et
observavit Leydæ illustr. Gaubius. *Patholog. instit.* 751,
et in loquela hæc *volubilitas* dicitur quâ lingua præcur-
rit mentem. Video actu mulierem sexagenariam hoc
affectam morbo siccitati nervorum tribuendo; laborat
enim rheumatismo sicco, seu ab acrimonia sanguinis,
dolores nocte a calore recrudescunt, à thermis non sub-
levantur: ei præscripsi phlebotomiam, et præmissis jus-
culis ex lactucâ, endiviâ, et collo arietis, lene cathar-
ticum, inde vero lacticinia.

Est affinitas cum scelotyrbe, chorea viti, deest flexibi-
litas in fibris musculorum; unde motus breves edunt,
et conatu seu impetu solito majori, cum resistentiam
illam superare nituntur, velut inviti festinant, ac præcipiti
seu concitato passu gradiuntur. Chorea viti pueros,
puellasve impuberes aggreditur; festinia vero senes,
et duos tantum hactenus observare mihi contigit. Quam
multos autem videmus morbos, paucissimosque obser-
vamus. De theoriâ et pràxi nihil habeo quod dicam;
etenim sola experienta praxim cujusvis morbi deter-
minat, et ex hac pro felici vel infausto successu theoria
dein elicienda est. *Nosolog. Methodic.* Auctore, Fr.
Boissier de Sauvages. Tomi. II. Part ii. p. 108.

Having made the necessary inquiries respecting these two affections, *Tremor coactum* of Sylvius de la Boë and of Sauvages, and *Scelotyrbe festinans* of the latter nosologist, which appear to be characteristic symptoms of this disease, it becomes necessary, in the next place, to endeavour to distinguish this disease from others which may bear a resemblance to it in some particular respects.

CHAP. III.

SHAKING PALSY DISTINGUISHED FROM OTHER DISEASES WITH WHICH IT MAY BE CONFOUNDED.

TREATING of a disease resulting from an assemblage of symptoms, some of which do not appear to have yet engaged the general notice of the profession, particular care is required whilst endeavouring to mark its diagnostic characters. It is sufficient, in general, to point out the characteristic differences which are observable between diseases in some respects resembling each other. But in this case more is required : it is necessary to show that it is a disease which does not accord with any which are marked in the systematic arrangements of nosologists; and that the name by which it is here distinguished has been hitherto vaguely applied to diseases very different from each other, as well as from that to which it is now appropriated.

Palsy, either consequent to compression of the brain, or dependent on partial exhaustion of the energy of that organ, may, when the palsied limbs become affected with tremulous motions, be confounded with this disease. In those cases the abolition or diminution of voluntary muscular action takes place suddenly, the sense of feeling being sometimes also impaired. But in this disease, the diminution of the influence of the will on the muscles comes on with extreme slowness, is always accompanied, and even preceded, by agitations of the affected parts, and never by a lessened sense of feeling. The dictates of the will are even, in the last stages of the disease, conveyed to the muscles; and the muscles act on this impulse, but their actions are perverted.

Anomalous cases of convulsive affections

have been designated by the term Shaking
Palsy : a term which appears to be impro-
perly applied to these cases, independent
of the want of accordance between them
and that disease which has been here deno-
minated Shaking Palsy. Dr. Kirkland, in
his commentary on Apoplectic and Paralytic
Affections, &c. cites the following case, related by Dr. Charlton, as belonging, he says,
to the class of Shaking Palsies. " Mary
Ford, of a sanguineous and robust constitu-
tion, had an involuntary motion of her right
arm, occasioned by a fright, which first
brought on convulsion fits, and most excru-
ciating pain in the stomach, which vanished
on a sudden, and her right arm was instan-
taneously flung into an involuntary and
perpetual motion, like the swing of a pen-
dulum, raising the hand, at every vibration
higher than her head ; but if by any means
whatever it was stopped ; the pain in her
stomach came on again, and convulsion fits
were the certain consequence, which went
off when the vibration of her hand returned."

Another case, which the Doctor designates
as ' A Shaking Palsy,' apparently from worms,
he describes thus, " A poor boy, about

twelve or thirteen years of age, was seized
with a Shaking Palsy. His legs became
useless, and together with his head and
hands, were in continual agitation; after
many weeks trial of various remedies, my
assistance was desired.

" His bowels being cleared, I ordered
him a grain of Opium a day in the gum
pill; and in three or four days the shaking
had nearly left him." By pursuing this
plan, the medicine proving a vermifuge, he
could soon walk, and was restored to per-
fect health.

Whether these cases should be classed
under Shaking Palsy or not, is necessary
to be here determined; since, if they are
properly ranked, the cases which have been
described in the preceding pages, differ so
much from them as certainly to oppose their
being classed together: and the disease,
which is the subject of these pages, cannot be considered as the same with Shaking
Palsy, as characterised by those cases.

The term Shaking Palsy is evidently in-
applicable to the first of these cases, which

appears to have belonged more properly to the genus *Convulsio,* of Cullen, or to *Hieranosos* of Linnæus and Vogel *.

The latter appears to be referable to that class of proteal forms of disease, generated by a disordered state of primæ viæ, sympa-

* Corporis agitatio continua, indolens, convulsiva, cum sensibilitate.—*Linn.*

Agitatio corporis vel artuum convulsiva continua, chronica, cum integritate sensuum.—*Vogel.*

This genus is resolved by Cullen into that of Convulsio. *Synops. Nosol.* 1803.

Dr. Macbride has given a very interesting and illustrative case of this disease.

" Hieranasós, or Morbus Sacer, so called, as being vulgarly supposed to arise from witchcraft, or some extraordinary celestial influence, is a distinct genus of disease, though a very uncommon one ; the author once had an opportunity of seeing a case. The patient was a lad about seventeen, who at that time had laboured under this extraordinary disease for more than twelve years. His body was so distorted, and the legs and arms so twisted round it, by the continued convulsive working, that no words can give an adequate idea of the oddity of his figure ; the agitation of the muscles was perpetual ; but in general he did not complain of pain nor sickness ; and had his senses perfectly, insomuch that he used to assist his mother, who kept a little school, in teaching children to read." *A methodical Introduction to the Theory and Practice of Physic. By David Macbride, M. D. p.* 559

thetically affecting the nervous influence in
a distant part of the body.

Unless attention is paid to one circumstance, this disease will be confounded with
those species of passive tremblings to which
the term Shaking Palsies has frequently been
applied. These are, *tremor temulentus,* the
trembling consequent to indulgence in the
drinking of spirituous liquors; that which
proceeds from the immoderate employment
of tea and coffee; that which appears to be
dependent on advanced age; and all those
tremblings which proceed from the various
circumstances which induce a diminution of
power in the nervous system. But by attending to that circumstance alone, which
has been already noted as characteristic of
mere tremor, the distinction will readily
be made. If the trembling limb be supported, and none of its muscles be called
into action, the trembling will cease. In
the real Shaking Palsy the reverse of this
takes place, the agitation continues in full
force whilst the limb is at rest and unemployed; and even is sometimes diminished
by calling the muscles into employment.

CHAP. IV.

PROXIMATE CAUSE—REMOTE CAUSES—ILLUS-
TRATIVE CASES.

BEFORE making the attempt to point out the nature and cause of this disease, it is necessary to plead, that it is made under very unfavourable circumstances. Unaided by previous inquiries immediately directed to this disease, and not having had the advantage, in a single case, of that light which anatomical examination yields, opinions and not facts can only be offered. Conjecture founded on analogy, and an attentive consideration of the peculiar symptoms of the disease, have been the only guides that could be obtained for this research, the result of which is, as it ought to be, offered with hesitation.

SUPPOSED PROXIMATE CAUSE.

A diseased state of the *medulla spinalis*, in that part which is contained in the canal, formed by the superior cervical vertebræ, and extending, as the disease proceeds, to the *medulla oblongata.*

By the nature of the symptoms we are taught, that the disease depends on some irregularity in the direction of the nervous influence; by the wide range of parts which are affected, that the injury is rather in the source of this influence than merely in the nerves of the parts; by the situation of the parts whose actions are impaired, and the order in which they become affected, that the proximate cause of the disease is in the superior part of the medulla spinalis; and by the absence of any injury to the senses and to the intellect, that the morbid state does not extend to the encephalon.

Uncertainty existing as to the nature of the proximate cause of this disease, its remote causes must necessarily be referred to with indecision. Assuming however the state just mentioned as the proximate cause, it may be concluded that this may be the result of injuries of the medulla itself, or of the theca helping to form the canal in which it is inclosed.

The great degree of mobility in that portion of the spine which is formed by the superior cervical vertebræ, must render it, and the contained parts, liable to injury from sudden distortions. Hence therefore may proceed inflammation of quicker or of slower progress, disease of the vertebræ, derangement of structure in the medulla, or in its membranes, thickening or even ulceration of the theca, effusion of fluids, &c.

But in no case which has been noticed, has the patient recollected receiving any injury of this kind, or any fixed pain in early life in these parts, which might have led to the opinion that the foundation for this malady had been thus laid. On the subject indeed of remote causes, no satisfactory accounts has yet been obtained from any of the sufferers. Whilst one has attributed this affliction to indulgence in spirituous liquors, and another to long lying on the damp ground; the others have been unable to suggest any circumstance whatever, which, in their opinion, could be considered as having given origin, or disposed, to the calamity under which they suffered.

Cases illustrative of the nature and cause of this malady are very rare. In the following case symptoms very similar are observable, so far as affecting the lower extremities. That the medulla spinalis was here affected, and in its lower part, is not to be doubted : but this, unfortunately, was never ascertained by examination. It must be however remarked, that this case differed from those which have been given of this disease, in the suddenness with which the symptoms appeared.

A. B. aged twenty-six years, during a course of mercury for a venereal affection, was exposed to severely inclement weather, for several hours, and the next morning, complained of extreme pain in the back, and of total inability to employ voluntarily the muscles of the lower extremities, which were continually agitated with severe convulsive motions. The physician who attended him employed those means which seemed best calculated to relieve him ; but with no beneficial effect. The lower extremities were perpetually agitated with strong palpitatory motions, and, frequently, three or four times in a minute, suddenly raised with great vehemence two or three feet from the ground, either in a forward or oblique direction, striking one limb against the other, or against the chairs, tables, or any substance which stood in the way. To check these inordinate motions, no means were in the least effectual, except striking the thighs forcibly during the more violent convulsions. No advantage was derived from all the means which were employed during upwards of twelvemonths. Full ten years after this period, the unhappy subject of this malady was casually met in the street, shifting himself along, seated in a chair; the convulsive motions having ceased, and the limbs having become totally inert, and insensible to any impulse of the will.

It must be acknowledged, that in the well-known cases, described by Mr. Potts, of that kind of Palsy of the lower limbs which is frequently found to accompany a curvature of the spine, and in which a carious state of the vertebræ is found to exist, no instructive analogy is discoverable; slight convulsive motions may indeed happen in the disease proceeding from curvature of the spine ; but palpitating motions of the limbs, such as belong to the disease here described, do not appear to have been hitherto noticed.

Whilst striving to determine the nature and origin of this disease, it becomes necessary to give the following particulars of an interesting case of Palsy occasioned by a fall, attended with uncommon symptoms, related by Dr. Maty, in the third volume of the Medical Observations and Inquiries. The subject of this case, the Count de Lordat, had the misfortune to be overturned from a pretty high and steep bank. His head pitched against the top of the coach, and was bent from left to right; his left shoulder, arm, and especially his hand, were considerably bruised. At first he felt a good deal of pain along the left side of his neck, but neither then, nor at any other time, had he any faintings, vomitings, or giddiness.—On the sixth day he was let blood, on account of the pain in his shoulder and the contusion of his hand, which were then the only symptoms he

complained of, and of which he soon found
himself relieved.—Towards the beginning
of the following winter, he began to find
*a small impediment in uttering some words, and
his left arm appeared weaker.* In the following
spring, having suffered considerably from the
severities of the winter campaign, he found
*the difficulty in speaking, and in moving his left
arm, considerably increased.*—On employing
the thermal waters of Bourbonne, his speech
become freer, but, on his return to Paris,
the Palsy was increased, and the arm somewhat wasted.—In the beginning of the next
spring he went to Balaruc; when he became affected with *involuntary convulsive
motions all over the body.* The left arm
withered more and more, *a spitting began,*
and now it was *with difficulty that he uttered a
few words.* Frictions and sinapisms were
successively tried, and an issue, made by a
caustic, was kept open for some time without any effect; but no mention is made
of what part the issue was established in.

Soon after this, and three years and a half
after the fall, Doctor Maty first saw the patient, and gives the following description of

his situation. " A more melancholy object I never beheld. The patient, naturally a handsome, middle-sized, sanguine man, of a cheerful disposition, and an active mind, appeared much emaciated, stooping, and dejected. *He still walked alone with a cane, from one room to the other, but with great difficulty, and in a tottering manner;* his left hand and arm were much reduced, and would hardly perform any motion; *the right was somewhat benumbed, and he could scarcely lift it up to his head; his saliva was continually trickling out of his mouth, and he had neither the power of retaining it, nor of spitting it out freely.* What words he still could utter were monosyllables, and these came out, after much struggle, in a violent expiration, and with such a low voice and indistinct articulation, as hardly to be understood but by those who were constantly with him. He fetched his breath rather hard; his pulse was low, but neither accelerated nor intermitting. He took very little nourishment, could chew and swallow no solids, and even found great pain in getting down liquids. Milk was almost his only food; his body was rather loose, his urine natural, his sleep good, his senses, and the powers of his mind, unimpaired; he was attentive to, and sensible of every thing which was said in conversation, and shewed himself very desirous of joining in it; but was continually checked by the impediment in his speech, and the difficulty which his hearers were put to. Happily for him he was able to read, and as capable as ever of writing, as he shewed me, by putting into my hands an account of his present situation, drawn up by himself: and I am informed that he spent his time to the very last, in writing upon some of the most abstruse subjects."

This gentleman died about four years after the accident, when the body was examined by Dr. Bellett and Mons. Sorbier, who made the following report:

" We first examined the muscles of the tongue, which were found extenuated and of a loose texture. We observed no signs of compression in the lingual and brachial nerves, as high as their exit from the basis of the cranium and the vertebræ of the neck;

G

but they appeared to us more compact than they commonly are, being nearly tendinous. The dura mater was in a sound state, but the pia mater was full of blood and lymph; on it several hydatids, and towards the falx some marks of suppuration were observed. The ventricles were filled with water, and the plexus choroides was considerably enlarged, and stuffed with grumous blood. The cortical surface of the brain appeared much browner than usual, but neither the medullary part nor cerebellum were impaired. We chiefly took notice of the Medulla Oblongata, this was greatly enlarged, surpassing the usual size by more than one third. It was likewise more compact. The membranes, which, in their continuation, inclose the spinal marrow, were so tough that we found great difficulty in cutting through them, and we observed this to be the cause of the tendinous texture of the cervical nerves. The marrow itself had acquired such solidity as to elude the pressure of our fingers, it resisted as a callous body, and could not be bruised. This hardness was observed all along the vertebræ of the neck, but lessened by degrees, and

was not near so considerable in the vertebræ of the thorax. Though the patient
was but nine and thirty years old, the car-
tilages of the sternum were ossified, and required as much labour to cut them asunder
as the ribs; like these they were spungy,
but somewhat whiter. The lungs and heart
were sound. At the bottom of the stomach
appeared an inflammation, which increased
as it extended to the intestines. The ileum
looked of that dark and livid hue, which
is observed in membranous parts tending
to mortification. The colon was not above
an inch in diameter, the rectum was smaller
still, but both appeared sound.—From these
appearances, we were at no loss to fix the
cause of this gradual palsy in the alte-
ration of the medulla spinalis and oblongata."

Dr. Bellett offers the following explanation of these changes. "I conceive, that, by
this accident, the head being violently bent
to the right, the nervous membranes on
the left were excessively stretched and
irritated; that this cause extended by degrees to the spinal marrow, which being

thereby compressed, brought on the paralytic symptoms, not only of the left arm,
but at last in some measure also of the right.
This induration seems to have been occasioned by the constant afflux of the nutritive
juices, which were stopt at that place, and
deprived of their most liquid parts; the
grosser ones being unable to spread in the
boney cavity, by which they were confined,
could only acquire a greater solidity, and
change a soft body into a hard and nearly
osseous mass. This likewise accounts for
the increase of the medulla oblongata, which
being loaded with more juices than it could
send off, swelled in the same manner as the
branches of trees, which will grow of a mon-
strous size, when the sap that runs into them
is stopt in its progress. The medulla oblongata not growing so hard as the spinalis,
was doubtless owing to its not being confined in an osseous theca, but surrounded
with soft parts, which allowed it room to
spread. The obstruction from the bulk of
this substance must have affected the brain,
and probably induced the thickening of
the pia mater, the hydatids, and the beginning of suppuration, whereas the dura

mater, being of a harder texture, was not injured *."

In some of the symptoms which appeared in this case, an agreement is observable between it and those cases which are mentioned in the beginning of these pages. The weakened state of both arms; the power first lessening in one arm, and then in a similar manner in the other arm; the affection of the speech; the difficulty in chewing and in swallowing; as well as of retaining, or freely discharging, the spittle; the convulsive motions of the body; and the unimpaired state of the intellects; constitute such a degree of accordance as, although it may not mark an identity of disease, serves at least to show that nearly the same parts were the seat of the disease in both instances. Thus we attain something like confirmation of the supposed proximate cause, and of one of the assumed occasional causes.

Whilst conjecturing as to the cause of this disease, the following collected obser-

* Medical Observations and Inquiries, Vol. III. p. 257.

vations on the effects of injury to the medulla spinalis, by Sir Everard Home, become particularly deserving of attention. It thence appears, that none of the characteristic symptoms of this malady are produced by compression, laceration, or complete division of the medulla spinalis.

" Pressure upon the medulla spinalis of the neck, by coagulated blood, produced paralytic affections of the arms and legs; all the functions of the internal organs were carried on for thirty-five days, but the urine and stools passed involuntarily *.

" Blood extravasated in the central part of the medulla, in the neck, was attended with paralytic affection of the legs, but not of the arms†.

* A coagulum of blood, the thickness of a crown-piece, was found lying upon the external surface of the dura-matral covering of the medulla spinalis, extending from the fourth vertebra colli to the second vertebra dorsi. The medulla spinalis itself was uninjured.

† The sixth and seventh vertebra colli were dislocated, the medulla spinalis, externally, was uninjured; but in the centre of its substance, just at that part, there was a coagulum of blood nearly two inches in length.

" In a case where the substance of the medulla was lacerated in the neck, there was
a paralysis in all the parts below the laceration, the lining of the œsophagus was so
sensible, that solids could not be swallowed,
on account of the pain they occasioned *.

" When the medulla of the back was completely divided, there was momentary loss
of sight, loss of memory for fifteen minutes,
and permanent insensibility in all the lower
parts of the body. The skin above the
division of the spinal marrow perspired, that
below did not. The wounded spinal marrow appeared to be extremely sensible †."
Philosophical Transactions, 1816, p. 485.

In two of the cases already noticed,
symptoms of rheumatism had previously
existed ; and in Case IV. the right arm, in
which the palpitation began, was said to

---

* The seventh vertebra colli was fractured, and the
medulla spinalis passing through it, was lacerated and
compressed.

† The spinal marrow, within the canal of the sixth
vertebra dorsi, was completely destroyed by a musket
ball. The person lived four days.

have been very violently affected with rheumatic pain to the fingers ends. The consideration of this case, in which the palpitation had been preceded, at a considerable distance of time, by this painful affection of the arm, led to the supposition that this latter circumstance might be the cause of the palpitations, and the other subsequent symptoms of this disease. This supposition naturally occasioned the attention to be eagerly fixed on the following case; and of course influenced the mode of treatment which was adopted.

A. B. subject to rheumatic affection of the deltoid muscle, had felt the usual inconveniences from it for two or three days; but at night found the pain had extended down the arm, along the inside of the fore-arm, and on the sides of the fingers, in which a continual tingling was felt. The pain, without being extremely intense, was such as effectually to prevent sleep: and seemed to follow the course of the brachial nerve. Whilst ascertaining the propriety of this conclusion, the pain was found to ramify, as it were, on the fore and back part of the

chest; and was slightly augmented by draw-
ing a deep breath.

These circumstances suggested the probability of slight inflammation, or increased
determination to the origin of the nerves of
these parts, and to the neighbouring medulla.
On this ground, blood was taken from the
back part of the neck, by cupping; hot
fomentations were applied for about the
space of an hour, when the upper part of the
back of the neck was covered with a blister,
perspiration was freely induced by two or
three small doses of antimonials, and the following morning the bowels were evacuated
by an appropriate dose of calomel. On the
following day the pains were much diminished, and in the course of four or five days
were quite removed. The arm and hand felt
now more than ordinarily heavy, and were
evidently much weakened : aching, and feeling extremely wearied after the least exertion. The strength of the arm was not
completely recovered at the end of more
than twelvemonths; and, after more than
twice that time, exertion would excite the
feeling of painful weariness, but no palpi-

H

tation or other unpleasant symptom has occurred during the five or six years which
have since passed.

The commencement, progress, and termination of this attack; with the success
attending the mode of treatment, and the
symptoms which followed, seem to lead to
the conjecture, that the proximate cause of
the disease, in this case, existed in the medulla spinalis, and that it might, if neglected,
have gradually resolved itself into that disease which is the object of our present inquiry.

Some few months after the occurrence of
the preceding case, the writer of these lines
was called to a female about forty years of
age, complaining of great pain in both the
arms, extending from the shoulder to the
finger ends. She stated, that she was attacked in the same manner as is described
in the preceding case, about nine months
before; that the complaint was considered
as rheumatism, and was not benefited by
any of the medicines which had been employed; but that after three or four weeks

it gradually amended, leaving both the arms and hands in a very weakened and trembling state. From this state they were now somewhat recovered; but she was extremely anxious, fearing that if the present attack should not be soon checked, she might entirely lose the use of her hands and arms.

Instructed by the preceding case, similar means were here recommended. Leeches, stimulating fomentations, and a blister, which was made for sometime to yield a purulent discharge, were applied over the cervical vertebræ; and in the course of a very few days the pain was entirely removed. It is regretted that no farther information, as to the progress of this case, could be obtained.

On meeting with these two cases, it was thought that it might not be improbable that attacks of this kind, considered at the time merely as rheumatic affections, might lay the foundation of this lamentable disease, which might manifest itself at some distant period, when the circumstance in which it had originated, had, perhaps, almost escaped

the memory. Indeed when it is considered
that neither in the ordinary cases of Palsy
of the lower extremities, proceeding from
diseased spine, nor in cases of injured medulla from fractured vertebræ, any of the
peculiar symptoms of this disease are observable, we necessarily doubt as to the probability of its being the direct effect of any
sudden injury. But taking all circumstances
into due consideration, particularly the very
gradual manner in which the disease com-
mences, and proceeds in its attacks ; as well
as the inability to ascribe its origin to any
more obvious cause, we are led to 'seek for
it in some slow morbid change in the structure of the medulla, or its investing membranes, or theca, occasioned by simple inflammation, or rheumatic or scrophulous
affection.

It must be too obvious that the evidence
adduced as to the nature of the proximate
and occasional causes of this disease, is by no
means conclusive. A reference to the test
therefore which will be yielded by an examination of some of the more prominent
symptoms, especially as to their agreement

with the supposed proximate cause, is more particularly demanded. Satisfied as to the importance of this part of the present undertaking, no apology is offered for the extent to which the examination is carried on.

If the palpitation and the attendant weakness of the limbs, &c. be considered as to the order in which the several parts are attacked, it is believed, that some confirmation will be obtained of the opinion which has been just offered, respecting the cause, or at least the seat, of that change which may be considered as the proximate cause of this disease.

One of the arms, in all the cases which have been here mentioned, has been the part in which these symptoms have been first noticed; the legs, head, and trunk have then become gradually affected, and lastly, the muscles of the mouth and fauces have yielded to the morbid influence.

The arms, the parts first manifesting disordered action, of course direct us, whilst searching for the cause of these changes, to the brachial nerves. But finding the mischief extending to other parts, not supplied with these, but with other nerves derived from nearly the same part of the medulla spinalis, we are of course led to consider that portion of the medulla spinalis itself, from which these nerves are derived, as the part in which those changes have taken place, which constitute the proximate cause of this disease.

From the subsequent affection of the lower extremities, and from the failure of power in the muscles of the trunk, such a change in the substance of the medulla spinalis may be inferred, as shall have considerably interrupted, and interfered with, the extension of the nervous influence to those parts, whose nerves are derived from any portion of the medulla below the part which has undergone the diseased change.

The difficulty in supporting the trunk erect, as well as the propensity to the adopting of a hurried pace, is also referable to such a diminution of the nervous power in the extensor muscles of the head and trunk, as prevents them from performing the offices of maintaining the head and body in an erect position.

From the impediment to speech, the difficulty in mastication and swallowing, the inability to retain, or freely to eject, the Saliva, may with propriety be inferred an extension of the morbid change upwards through the medulla spinalis to the medulla oblongata, necessarily impairing the powers of the several nerves derived from that portion into which the morbid change may have reached. In the late occurrence of this set of symptoms, and the extension upwards of the diseased state, a very close agreement is observable between this disease and that which has been already shown, proved fatal to the Count de Lordat. But in this case, the disease doubtlessly became differently modified, and its symptoms considerably accelerated, in consequence of the magnitude of the injury by which the disease was induced.

CHAP. V.

CONSIDERATIONS RESPECTING THE MEANS OF CURE.

THE inquiries made in the preceding pages yield, it is to be much regretted, but little more than evidence of inference : nothing direct and satisfactory has been obtained. All that has been ventured to assume here, has been that the disease depends on a disordered state of that part of the medulla which is contained in the cervical vertebræ. But of what nature that morbid change is; and whether originating in the medulla itself, in its membranes, or in the containing theca, is, at present, the subject of doubt and conjecture. But although, at present, uninformed as to the precise nature of the disease, still it ought not to be considered as one against which there exists no countervailing remedy.

On the contrary, there appears to be sufficient reason for hoping that some remedial process may ere long be discovered, by which, at least, the progress of the disease may be

stopped. It seldom happens that the agitation extends beyond the arms within the
first two years; which period, therefore,
if we were disposed to divide the disease
into stages, might be said to comprise the
first stage. In this period, it is very probable, that remedial means might be employed with success: and even, if unfortunately deferred to a later period, they
might then arrest the farther progress of
the disease, although the removing of the
effects already produced, might be hardly
to be expected.

From a review of the changes which had
taken place in the case of Count de Lordat, it
seems as if we were able to trace the order
and mode in which the morbid changes
may proceed in this disease. From any
occasional cause, the thecal ligament, the
membranes, or the medulla itself, may pass
into the state of simple excitement or irri-
tation, which may be gradually succeeded
by such a local afflux and determination of
blood into the minute vessels, as may ter-
minate in actual but slow inflammation.
The result of this would be a thickening

of the theca, or membranes, and perhaps an increase in the volume of the medulla itself, which would gradually occasion such a degree of pressure against the sides of the unyielding canal, as must eventually intercept the influence of the brain upon the inferior portion of the medullary column, and upon the parts on which the nerves of this portion are disposed.

From this review, and assuming that the morbid changes in this disease may not be widely dissimilar from those which occurred in the case of Count de Lordat, the chance of relief from the proposed mode of treatment may appear to be sufficient to warrant its trial.

In such a case then, at whatever period of the disease it might be proposed to attempt the cure, blood should be first taken from the upper part of the neck, unless contra-indicated by any particular circumstance. After which vesicatories should be applied to the same part, and a purulent discharge obtained by appropriate use of the Sabine Liniment; having recourse to

the application of a fresh blister, when from
the diminution of the discharging surface,
pus is not secreted in a sufficient quantity.
Should the blisters be found too inconve-
nient, or a sufficient quantity of discharge not
be obtained thereby, an issue of at least an
inch and a half in length might be established on each side of the vertebral co-
lumna, in its superior part. These, it is
presumed, would be best formed with caustic,
and kept open with any proper substance *.

Could it have been imagined that such
considerable benefit: indeed, that such
astonishing cures, could have been effected
by issues in cases of Palsy of the lower extremities from diseased spine? although satisfied with ascribing those cases to scrofu-
lous action, we are in fact as little informed
respecting the nature of the affection, in-

* Cork, which has been hitherto neglected, appears
to be very appropriate to this purpose. It possesses
lightness, softness, elasticity and sufficient firmness; and
is also capable of being readily fashioned to any conve-
nient form. The form which it seems would be best
adapted to the part, is that of an almond, or of the va-
riety of bean called scarlet bean; but at least an inch
and a half in length.

ducing the carious state of the vertebræ, as
we are respecting the peculiar change of
structure which takes place in this disease.
Equally uninformed are we also as to the
peculiar kind of morbid action, which takes
place in the ligaments of the joints; as well
as that which takes place in different instances of deep seated pains and affections
of the parts contained in the head, thorax,
and abdomen, and in all which cases the
inducing of a purulent discharge in their
neighbourhood is so frequently productive of
a cure. Experiment has not indeed been yet
employed to prove, but analogy certainly
warrants the hope, that similar advantages
might be derived from the use of the means
enumerated, in the present disease. It is
obvious, that the chance of obtaining relief
will depend in a great measure on the period at which the means are employed. As
in every other disease, so here, the earlier
the remedies are resorted to, the greater will
be the probability of success. But in this
disease there is one circumstance which de-
mands particular attention ; the long period
to which it may be extended. One of its
peculiar symptoms, Scelotyrbe festinans, may

not occur until the disease has existed ten or twelve years, or more ; hence, when looking for the period, within which our hopes of remedial aid is to be limited; we may, guided by the slow progress of the malady, extend it to a great length, when compared with that within which we should be obliged to confine ourselves in most other diseases.

But it is much to be apprehended, as in many other cases, that the resolution of the patients will seldom be sufficient to enable them to persevere through the length of time which the proposed process will necessarily require. As slow as is the progress of the disease, so slow in all probability must be the period of the return to health. In most cases, especially in those in which the disease has been allowed to exist long unopposed, it may be found that all that art is capable of accomplishing, is that of checking its further progress. Nor will this be regarded as a trifle, when, by reference to the history of the disease, is seen the train of harassing evils which would be thus avoided.

But.it seems as if there existed reason for hoping for more. For supposing change of structure to have taken place, it is extremely probable that this change may be merely increase in mass or volume by interstitial addition, the consequence of increased action in the minute vessels of the part. In that case, should the instituting of a purulent discharge, in a neighbouring part, act in the manner which we would presume it may—should it by keeping up a constant discharge, not merely alter the determination, but diminish the inordinate action of the vessels in the diseased part; and at the same time excite the absorbents to such increased action as may remove the added matter; there will exist strong ground for hope, that a happy, though slow restoration to health, may be obtained.

Until we are better informed respecting the nature of this disease, the employment of internal medicines is scarcely warrantable; unless analogy should point out some remedy the trial of which rational hope might authorize. Particular circumstances indeed must arise in different cases, in which the aid of medicine may be demanded : and the intelligent will never fail to avail themselves of any opportunity of making trial of the influence of mercury, which has in so many instances, manifested its power in correcting derangement of structure.

The weakened powers of the muscles in the affected parts is so prominent a symptom, as to be very liable to mislead the inattentive, who may regard the disease as a mere consequence of constitutional debility. If this notion be pursued, and tonic medicines, and highly nutritious diet be directed, no benefit is likely to be thus obtained ; since the disease depends not on general weakness, but merely on the interruption of the flow of the nervous influence to the affected parts.

It is indeed much to be regretted that this malady is generally regarded by the sufferers in this point of view, so discouraging to the employment of remedial means. Seldom occurring before the age of fifty, and frequently yielding but little inconvenience for several months, it is generally considered as the irremediable diminution of the nervous influence, naturally resulting from declining life ; and remedies therefore are seldom sought for.

Although unable to trace the connection by which a disordered state of the stomach and bowels may induce a morbid action in a part of the medulla spinalis, yet taught by the instruction of Mr. Abernethy, little hesitation need be employed before we determine on the probability of such occurrence. The power, possessed by sympathy, of inducing such disordered action in a distant part, and the probability of such disordered action producing derangement of structure, can hardly be denied. The following Case seems to prove, at least, that the mysterious sympathetic influence which so closely simulates the forms of other diseases, may induce such symptoms as would seem to menace the formation of a disease not unlike to that which we have been here treating of.

A. B. A man, 54 years of age, of temperate habits and regular state of bowels, became gradually affected with slight numbness and prickling, with a feeling of weakness in both arms, accompanied by a sense of fulness about the shoulders, as if produced by the pressure of a strong ligature; and at times a slight trembling of the hands. During the night, the fullness, numbness, and prickling were much increased. The appetite had been diminished for several weeks; and the abdomen, on being examined, felt as though containing considerable accumulation.

Before adopting any other measures, and as there appeared to be no marks of vascular fulness, it was determined to empty the bowels. This was done effectually by moderate doses of calomel, with the occasional help of Epsom salts; and in about ten days, by these means alone, the complaints were entirely removed.

Before concluding these pages, it may be proper to observe once more, that an important object proposed to be obtained by them is, the leading of the attention o those who humanely employ anatomical examination in detecting the causes and nature of diseases, particularly to this malady. By their benevolent labours its real nature may be ascertained, and appropriate modes of relief, or even of cure, pointed out.

To such researches the healing art is already much indebted for the enlargement of its powers of lessening the evils of suffering humanity. Little is the public aware of the obligations it owes to those who, led by professional ardour, and the dictates of duty, have devoted themselves to these pursuits, under circumstances most unpleasant and forbidding. Every person of consideration and feeling, may judge of the advantages yielded by the philanthropic exertions of a HOWARD; but how few can estimate the benefits bestowed on mankind, by the labours of a MORGAGNI, HUNTER, or BAILLIE.

FINIS.

THE

FOLLOWING WORKS,

BY

JAMES PARKINSON,

SOLD BY

SHERWOOD, NEELY, AND JONES, PATERNOSTER-ROW.

1. ORGANIC REMAINS of a FORMER WORLD; or, an Examination of the Mineralized Remains of the Vegetables and Animals of the Antediluvian World, generally termed Extraneous Fossils. In three Volumes quarto.

Vol. I. containing the Vegetable Kingdom, price £.3 13 6
—— II. containing the Fossil Zoophytes............ 3 3 0
—— III. containing the Fossil Starfish, Echini, Shells,
  Insects, Amphibia, Mammalia, &c.......... 3 13 6

The whole illustrated with 53 Plates, accurately engraved by Springsguth, and coloured in imitation of the Originals.

In almost every part of this globe, the remains of a former world are continually offering themselves for the contemplation of mankind; teaching, that the planet we inhabit has suffered considerable changes by the influence of causes, acting with vast power, and to a wide extent. Among these remains, the spoils of the vegetables and animals of former days are frequently discovered; evincing that several beings then existed, which are now entirely unknown, and perhaps extinct; their mutilated remains only being left to prove, that they once lived, and were destroyed with former worlds.

These medals of nature, yielding incontestable records of the most important æra in the history of the universe, exist in great quantities in this island: but whilst France and Germany have produced several valuable essays on these important subjects, Great Britain owned not a single systematic work on this branch of natural history. Reflection on this circumstance led to the present attempt to form a history of all those bodies which have been hitherto discovered; trusting that encouragement to such an undertaking will be secured by the laudable curiosity of those who dwell in those parts, where these wonderful relics of the Old World are, even by accident, daily brought to view.

2. MEDICAL ADMONITIONS TO FAMILIES, respecting the Preservation of Health, and the Treatment of the Sick; also a Table of Symptoms, serving to point out the Degrees of Danger, and to distinguish one Disease from another; with Observations on the improper indulgence of Children, &c. Fifth Edition, greatly enlarged.—Price 10s. boards.

In this work are shown the dangers of domestic Quackery, the necessity for application for relief in the first stages of disease, and the means to be employed in the moments of emergency, and in the absence of the medical practitioner.

3. HINTS FOR THE IMPROVEMENT OF TRUSSES, Price 9d.

4. THE VILLAGER'S FRIEND AND PHYSICIAN; or, a Familiar Address on the Preservation of Health, and the Removal of Disease on its first Appearance. With Cursory Observations on the Treatment of Children, on Sobriety, Industry, &c. Intended for the Promotion of Domestic Happiness. Second Edition, with a Frontispiece. Price 1s. 6d.

5. THE WAY TO HEALTH; a Selection of Maxims for the Preservation of Health, extracted from the Villager's Friend; and printed on a Single Sheet, for the Cottager's Fire Side. Embellished with an emblematical Print. Price 6d.

6. DANGEROUS SPORTS, a Tale, addressed to Children, warning them against wanton, careless, or mischievous Exposure to Situations from which alarming Injuries so often proceed. Embellished with a Frontispiece and Eleven Wood Cuts. Price 2s. 6d. Vellum.

7. THE CHEMICAL POCKET BOOK; or, Memoranda Chemica. Arranged in a Compendium of Chemistry; with appropriate Tables. A new Edition (the Fourth, Price 9s. boards) greatly improved by numerous and important Additions, particularly in Subjects connected with the Arts and Manufactures, as Dying, Tanning of Leather, Gilding, Painting, &c. &c.

8. THE HOSPITAL PUPIL; or, Observations addressed to the Parents of Youths intended for the Profession of Medicine or Surgery, on their previous Education, pecuniary Resources, and on the Order of their professional Studies; with Hints to the young Pupil on the Prosecution of Hospital Studies, on entering into Practice, and on Medical Jurisprudence. Second Edition. Price 5s.